GAULISH VILLAGE

COMPENDIUM

LAUDANUM

AQUARIUM

TOTORUM

ARMORICA

BELGICA

•LUTETIA

SPQR

GAUL
(ROMAN CONQUEST)
50 BC

CELTICA

AQUITANIA

PROVINCIA

THE YEAR IS 50 BC. GAUL IS ENTIRELY OCCUPIED BY THE
ROMANS. WELL, NOT ENTIRELY ... ONE SMALL VILLAGE OF
INDOMITABLE GAULS STILL HOLDS OUT AGAINST THE INVADERS.
AND LIFE IS NOT EASY FOR THE ROMAN LEGIONARIES WHO
GARRISON THE FORTIFIED CAMPS OF TOTORUM, AQUARIUM,
LAUDANUM AND COMPENDIUM ...

ASTERIX, THE HERO OF THESE ADVENTURES. A SHREWD, CUNNING LITTLE WARRIOR, ALL PERILOUS MISSIONS ARE IMMEDIATELY ENTRUSTED TO HIM. ASTERIX GETS HIS SUPERHUMAN STRENGTH FROM THE MAGIC POTION BREWED BY THE DRUID GETAFIX . . .

OBELIX, ASTERIX'S INSEPARABLE FRIEND. A MENHIR DELIVERY MAN BY TRADE, ADDICTED TO WILD BOAR. OBELIX IS ALWAYS READY TO DROP EVERYTHING AND GO OFF ON A NEW ADVENTURE WITH ASTERIX – SO LONG AS THERE'S WILD BOAR TO EAT, AND PLENTY OF FIGHTING. HIS CONSTANT COMPANION IS DOGMATIX, THE ONLY KNOWN CANINE ECOLOGIST, WHO HOWLS WITH DESPAIR WHEN A TREE IS CUT DOWN.

GETAFIX, THE VENERABLE VILLAGE DRUID, GATHERS MISTLETOE AND BREWS MAGIC POTIONS. HIS SPECIALITY IS THE POTION WHICH GIVES THE DRINKER SUPERHUMAN STRENGTH. BUT GETAFIX ALSO HAS OTHER RECIPES UP HIS SLEEVE . . .

CACOFONIX, THE BARD. OPINION IS DIVIDED AS TO HIS MUSICAL GIFTS. CACOFONIX THINKS HE'S A GENIUS. EVERY-ONE ELSE THINKS HE'S UNSPEAKABLE. BUT SO LONG AS HE DOESN'T SPEAK, LET ALONE SING, EVERYBODY LIKES HIM . . .

FINALLY, VITALSTATISTIX, THE CHIEF OF THE TRIBE. MAJESTIC, BRAVE AND HOT-TEMPERED, THE OLD WARRIOR IS RESPECTED BY HIS MEN AND FEARED BY HIS ENEMIES. VITALSTATISTIX HIMSELF HAS ONLY ONE FEAR, HE IS AFRAID THE SKY MAY FALL ON HIS HEAD TOMORROW. BUT AS HE ALWAYS SAYS, TOMORROW NEVER COMES.

ALL IS PEACEFUL IN THE LITTLE GAULISH VILLAGE WE KNOW SO WELL, AND, AS USUAL, EVERYONE IS CHEERFUL AND FRIENDLY...

GOOD MORNING, OBELIX, GOOD MORNING, DOGMATIX!

GOOD MORNING, ASTERIX!

WOOF!

GOOD MORNING, UNHYGIENIX!

GOOD MORNING, IMPEDIMENTA!

UNHYGIENIX FISHMONGER

GOOD MORNING, GERIATRIX!

GOOD MORNING, CACOFONIX! STILL LOST YOUR VOICE?

GOOD MORNING, MY BOY!

AND IN THE ROMAN SENATE, OLD SENATOR STRADIVARIUS IS GETTING ALL STRUNG UP. IN HIS WELL MODULATED TONES, CALCULATED TO ROUSE A CROWD TO FEVER PITCH, HE IS SETTLING AN OLD SCORE WITH CAESAR...

CAESAR STILL ASKS US FOR MONEY AND MEN TO WAGE WAR, AND YET HE'S NOT EVEN CAPABLE OF KEEPING THE PAX ROMANA IN THE COUNTRIES HE'S ALREADY CONQUERED! ...

...THERE'S A LITTLE VILLAGE UP THERE IN GAUL. IT DEFIES OUR OCCUPYING FORCES AND REFUSES TO OBEY OUR LAWS!

LET CAESAR ENFORCE THE POWER OF ROME IN THE OCCUPIED TERRITORIES BEFORE HE THINKS OF NEW CAMPAIGNS!

YES!

HEAR, HEAR!

FOR JUPITER'S SAKE, GET THAT PLEB A SEAT!

A PLEBISCITE! GOOD IDEA!

SO THE NEXT DAY CAESAR HOLDS A MEETING OF HIS FRIENDS AND COLLEAGUES AT HIS LUXURIOUS VILLA OUTSIDE ROME.

MON REPOS

MEA REQVIES

CAVE CANEM

BEWARE OF THE DOG

1

AH, THERE YOU ARE AT LAST, BRUTUS! SIT DOWN. NOW WE CAN BEGIN.

THE ROADS ARE SO BUSY AFTER THE CALENDS...

THE SENATE WANTS TO TAKE ITS REVENGE ON ME FOR CUTTING ITS POWER. I MUST SHOW THEM WHO'S THE BOSS, AND TO DO THAT I'LL HAVE TO WIPE OUT THIS WRETCHED GAULISH VILLAGE...

LET'S HAVE YOUR IDEAS... SPEAK UP.

ET TU, BRUTE.

I SUGGEST BRUTE FORCE!

THEY HAVE A MAGIC POTION WHICH MAKES THEM INVINCIBLE. AND DO PUT THAT DAGGER AWAY, YOU IDIOT, YOU'LL DO YOURSELF AN INJURY!

STOP ME IF I'M ON THE WRONG TRACK, BUT WHAT ABOUT BUYING THEM OFF?

THESE BARBARIANS ARE NOT INTERESTED IN MONEY. IF THEY WERE, THE MAGIC POTION WOULD HAVE BEEN ON THE MARKET LONG AGO!

THIS IS ONLY A SUGGESTION, BUT...

...THEIR STRENGTH SPRINGS FROM THEIR SOLIDARITY. IF WE COULD SOW A BIT OF DISCORD IN THE VILLAGE, THEY WOULD SPLIT UP AND THE POTION WOULDN'T MATTER ANY MORE...

I KNOW THE GAULS ARE FAMOUS FOR THEIR INCESSANT ARGUMENTS, BUT THIS LOT STICK TOGETHER THROUGH THICK AND THIN.

J.C.! I'VE GOT THE VERY MAN! HE'LL SPLIT THEM UP FOR YOU!

HE USED TO HAVE A FLAT IN AN INSULA* I OWN. HE MADE SO MUCH TROUBLE IN THE BUILDING THAT THE OTHER TENANTS MANAGED TO GET HIM THROWN INTO PRISON TO BE EATEN BY THE LIONS!

* BLOCK OF FLATS

WHERE IS THIS TROUBLEMAKER OF YOURS?

HE'S STILL IN PRISON. WHEN THEY PUT HIM IN THE ARENA, THE LIONS ATE ONE ANOTHER!

HAVE HIM BROUGHT TO ME! NOW FOR SOME FOOD. ET TU, BRUTE!

THESE CLASSICAL ALLUSIONS ARE BEGINNING TO GET ON MY NERVES! ONE OF THESE DAYS I'LL...

MEANWHILE, THINGS ARE MUCH THE SAME IN THE LITTLE GAULISH VILLAGE...

LIFE'S GOOD, O DRUID!

TOO GOOD, ASTERIX! THE ROMANS ARE BEHAVING THEMSELVES, WE HAVEN'T GOT ANY WORRIES, OUR BARD HAS LOST HIS VOICE – IT CAN'T LAST... I FEEL THERE'S TROUBLE BREWING.

OUR DRUID'S CHANGED! HE'S GETTING PESSIMISTIC IN HIS OLD AGE.

HOWEVER, THE DRUID'S PREMONITION IS NOT WITHOUT FOUNDATION. DANGER IS PLOUGHING ITS WAY TOWARDS GAUL ON BOARD A ROMAN GALLEY WHERE EVERYONE IS ARGUING, FROM THE CAPTAIN...

WELL NOW, ABERDEENANGUS, SO IT SEEMS I'M NOTHING BUT AN OLD AMPHORA OF WINE?

I NEVER SAID THAT, CAP'N! IT WAS GIANTORTUS WHO SAID THAT!

...DOWN TO THE GALLEY SLAVES.

WAS IT YOU WHO TOLD THE OTHER LADS I WASN'T PULLING MY WEIGHT?

SHUT UP AND ROW!

WELL, GIANTORTUS DID SAY THAT IT WAS YOU WHO SAID I WAS NOTHING BUT AN OLD AMPHORA OF WINE!

AND I SAY THAT IF GIANTORTUS SAID THAT, GIANTORTUS IS A LIAR!

PIRATE SHIP TO PORT!

DID YOU HEAR THAT, CAPTAIN?

NO! NO ONE'S TO LISTEN TO HIM! HE'S BEEN SENT TO COVENTRIUM!

HE DARED TO SAY THAT WHILE WE WERE AT SEA OUR WIVES WERE ALL OUT AT ORGIES!

?!?

IF THAT'S THE WAY THE LAND LIES, I SHAN'T SAY ANOTHER WORD!!!

HUH! THEY'RE THE SORT OF PEOPLE WHO'D SAY I ONLY GOT INTO THE NAVY BECAUSE MY WIFE IS A CLOSE FRIEND OF JULIUS CAESAR'S SECOND COUSIN TWICE REMOVED!

IN THE LITTLE GAULISH VILLAGE, IN CONTRAST TO THESE VIOLENT EVENTS...

WE'RE GOING TO GET THINGS READY FOR CHIEF VITALSTATISTIX'S BIRTHDAY PARTY.

IT WILL BE AN OCCASION OF GENERAL GOODWILL!

THERE'LL BE HEAPS OF BOAR FULL OF BONES, DOGMATIX!

I'M GOING TO GIVE THE CHIEF A MENHIR. WHAT ABOUT YOU?

A SHIELD FOR HIS COLLECTION!

I'M GOING TO GIVE HIM A SWORD!

I'M GOING TO GIVE HIM A FISH. HE CAN STUFF IT!

DON'T LET ON! REMEMBER, WE WANT TO GIVE VITALSTATISTIX A NICE SURPRISE...

WHAT A WONDERFUL SURPRISE! MY DEAR FRIENDS...

...I AM AT A LOSS FOR WORDS, BUT LET ME TRY TO EXPRESS ALL THE JOY I FEEL...

YOU COULD HELP ME PLUCK THIS CHICKEN, INSTEAD OF SPOUTING SUCH RUBBISH!

IMPEDIMENTA, IN MY POSITION AS CHIEF, AS THE MOST IMPORTANT MAN IN THE VILLAGE, I DO HAVE CERTAIN OBLIGATIONS...

YES, WHEN IT COMES TO STUFFING YOURSELF WITH FOOD AND DRINK ANY EXCUSE WILL DO, BUT WHEN IT COMES TO WORKING...

WELL, YOU'RE PROUD OF BEING THE CHIEF'S WIFE, AREN'T YOU? FIRST LADY OF THE VILLAGE! SOME OF MY GLORY RUBS OFF ON TO YOU!

YOU CAN SAY THAT AGAIN! WE'RE GOING TO BE LANDED WITH A LOT OF STUPID PRESENTS. WE COULD NEVER EXPECT YOUR FRIENDS TO GIVE YOU ANYTHING WORTHWHILE, OH NO! NO ARTISTIC SENSE! JUST SAVAGES...

IN THE TENT OF THE CENTURION IN COMMAND OF THE ROMAN CAMP OF AQUARIUM...

...AND THAT POTION OF THEIRS MUST BE STRONG STUFF – THEY'RE FULL OF TEAM SPIRIT!

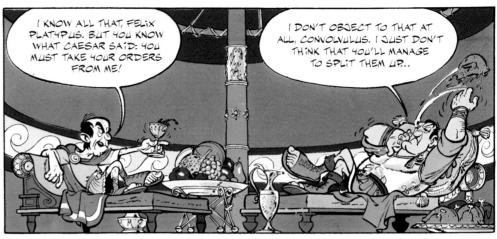

I KNOW ALL THAT, FELIX PLATYPUS. BUT YOU KNOW WHAT CAESAR SAID: YOU MUST TAKE YOUR ORDERS FROM ME!

I DON'T OBJECT TO THAT AT ALL, CONVOLVULUS. I JUST DON'T THINK THAT YOU'LL MANAGE TO SPLIT THEM UP...

YOU HAVE GIVEN ME THE NAME AND DESCRIPTION OF EVERY ONE OF THOSE NUT CASES. NOW, I NEED THAT!

THAT?

IT'S JUST THAT THIS VASE IS PART OF THE SPOILS FROM ONE OF MY CAMPAIGNS...

YES, YOUR JUNIOR OFFICERS TOLD ME YOU HAD SOME INDIVIDUAL IDEAS ABOUT SHARING OUT THE BOOTY.

GET ALL MY JUNIOR OFFICERS FALLEN IN!

SOON AFTERWARDS...

WHAT D'YOU WANT, ROMAN?

I HAVE BROUGHT A PRESENT TO THE MOST IMPORTANT MAN IN THE VILLAGE!

...AND HE'S BROUGHT A VALUABLE VASE!

AH!

?

PORTERS!

CLICK...

HERE HE COMES! RIGHT, BOYS! SHOW A BIT OF DIGNITY! WE DON'T WANT TO LOOK AS IF WE'RE EXPECTING HIM!

13

HAVING ARRIVED LATELY IN GAUL, AND DESIROUS OF STRENGTHENING THE TIES OF FRIENDSHIP BETWEEN ROMANS AND GAULS, I BRING THIS GIFT FOR YOU, THE MOST IMPORTANT MAN IN THE VILLAGE.

CHEERIO!

BACK HOME! JUMP TO IT!

AND HOW MANY TIMES DO I HAVE TO TELL YOU? BEND DOWN WHEN YOU GO THROUGH DOORWAYS!!!

IMPRESSIVE, EH? THE MOST IMPORTANT MAN IN THE VILLAGE, EH? THE ROMANS HAVE GOT THE PICTURE ALL RIGHT! AND THEY DON'T GIVE MENHIRS AND OTHER TRASH TO ASTERIX...

...REALLY IMPORTANT PEOPLE GET GIVEN VALUABLE WORKS OF ART!

I TELL YOU I'M THE MOST IMPORTANT!

OH YES? WELL, LET ME TELL YOU THAT IF ANYONE SHOULD EVER BE FOOL ENOUGH TO WRITE THE STORY OF OUR VILLAGE, THEY WON'T BE CALLING IT THE ADVENTURES OF VITALSTATISTIX THE GAUL!!!

I HOPE I'M NOT LATE?

OF COURSE NOT.

NOT TOO MUCH, JUST A LITTLE!

OH, IT'S ONLY MILK, SUGAR, EGGS, FLOUR AND BOAR FAT – NOT AT ALL FATTENING.

IMPEDIMENTA, ABOUT THIS MORNING... IT WAS ONLY A BIT OF FUN... A JOKE.

OF COURSE! LET'S TALK ABOUT MORE IMPORTANT THINGS...

MY HUSBAND THE CHIEF – JULIUS CAESAR NOMINATED HIM A SENATOR, BUT HE REFUSED, OF COURSE – WELL, HE'S GIVING A GREAT DEAL OF THOUGHT TO ASTERIX AND HIS FRIENDSHIP WITH THAT ROMAN.

YES, MY HUSBAND FULLIAUTOMATIX TOLD ME THEY WERE HAVING A GOOD TIME. HE HEARD LAUGHTER AND SINGING. THEY SEEMED TO HAVE BEEN DRINKING!

HOW DREADFUL! YOU KNOW, I'VE ALWAYS HAD MY DOUBTS ABOUT ASTERIX. A MAN OF HIS AGE, AND STILL A BACHELOR...

HOW OLD IS HE EXACTLY?

GOODNESS KNOWS! MY HUSBAND GERIATRIX SAYS HE'S NOT SO YOUNG AS HE LOOKS!

MMMM... AND HIS FRIEND OBELIX? DO YOU THINK HE'S A GOOD INFLUENCE? ALL THAT GREEDY PIG THINKS OF IS HIS FOOD!

THE TROUBLE IS THAT ASTERIX IS OUR DRUID GETAFIX'S FAVOURITE, AND HE KNOWS A LOT OF SECRETS...

THE SECRET OF THE MAGIC POTION, FOR EXAMPLE?

MY LIPS ARE SEALED.

AND SOON AFTERWARDS...

...SO ASTERIX HAS SOLD THE SECRET OF THE MAGIC POTION TO THE ROMANS? THESE YOUNG PEOPLE! I ASK YOU!

I'M WORRIED ABOUT THE VILLAGERS' ATTITUDE... SURELY THEY DON'T SUSPECT ME JUST BECAUSE OF THAT ROMAN'S VISIT?

HM... SLANDER CAN BE DANGEROUS. TOUTATIS ALONE KNOWS WHAT IDEAS THEY'RE DREAMING UP!

BUT NONE OF THAT MATTERS! THE CHIEF'S BIRTHDAY BANQUET IS THIS VERY EVENING. THAT WILL BRING EVERYBODY TOGETHER AGAIN.

BUT THE DRUID GETAFIX IS UNDULY OPTIMISTIC... IN THE VILLAGE, EVERYONE SUSPECTS EVERYONE ELSE...

THE ONLY ONE WHO IS UNAWARE OF THIS SAD STATE OF AFFAIRS IS THE BARD CACOFONIX, WITH HIS HEAD IN THE CLOUDS...

AND THAT EVENING DURING THE BANQUET, NO ONE IS SPEAKING TO ANYBODY ELSE...

!?!

...IN FACT, THE BARD HAS THE STRANGE IMPRESSION OF BEING ALONE AT THE TABLE. YOU MIGHT ALMOST THINK IT WAS THE END...

...THE END OF THE VILLAGE!

21

NEXT DAY, A ROMAN PATROL IS SCOUTING AROUND IN THE FOREST, TAKING NO CHANCES...

FOOTSTEPS!

LET'S HIDE IN THAT TREE OVER THERE!

OUCH! LET'S USE A DIFFERENT TREE!

THERE'S NO TIME! SSH!

IT'S VERY KIND OF YOU TO COME AND HELP ME CHECK MY SNARES, FULLIAUTOMATIX!

I WANTED A QUIET WORD WITH YOU, AWAY FROM THE OTHERS...

OUCH! SSH! OOH!

YOU'RE AN EXPERIENCED CHAP, GERIATRIX... IF THE ROMANS DO HAVE THE MAGIC POTION, IT'S VERY SERIOUS... MY WIFE THINKS THE TIME HAS COME TO LEAVE THE DISTRICT.

HUH! THE ROMANS DON'T SCARE ME WITH THEIR MAGIC POTION. I'M READY TO FIGHT AGAIN, AS WE DID AT GERGOVIA!

HAVE WE GOT THE MAGIC POTION?

SURELY WE'D KNOW!

BY THE WAY, BOYS, NOW THE GAULS HAVE GONE, SHALL WE GET DOWN FROM THIS TREE?

YES, BECAUSE OF THE WASPS!

BZZZZZZZZZZZZZZZ

BACK AT AQUARIUM...

WE'VE GOT THE MAGIC POTION! WE'VE GOT THE MAGIC POTION!!

???

CLINK!

I'VE CHOSEN YOU FOR THIS MISSION, MAGNUMOPUS, BECAUSE YOU HAVE ALL THE NECESSARY QUALITIES FOR PARTICIPATING IN PSYCHOLOGICAL WARFARE...

THE PATROL'S INTELLIGENCE IS CORRECT – A SNARE! EXCELLENT! LET'S HIDE BEHIND THIS TREE.

WHEN I GIVE THE SIGNAL, DO WHAT I TOLD YOU, MAGNUMOPUS...

HE'S ALONE! EVERYTHING'S GOING TO PLAN!

WHAT A PITY... NOTHING!

NOW!

BIFF!

EXCELLENT! NOW, TAKE YOUR HELMET OFF!

?

OFF WE GO!

DUH! I LIKES PSYCHOLOGICAL WARFARE, I DOES!

ALESIA! IT'S ALESIA ALL OVER AGAIN!

THEY'VE GOT THE MAGIC POTION!

THE ROMANS ATTACKED ME! THEY'VE GOT SUPER-HUMAN STRENGTH! I WASN'T BEATEN EASILY, AND I MANAGED TO SNATCH THIS TROPHY. ONLY THE MAGIC POTION COULD HAVE MADE THEM STRONG ENOUGH TO OVERCOME ME!

THAT PROVES IT! THEY'VE GOT THE POTION!

OUT OF THE QUESTION! ONLY OUR DRUID KNOWS ITS SECRET!

HE'S NOT THE ONLY ONE NOW!

HAVE YOU ALL GONE MAD, BY TOUTATIS? YOU DON'T NEED MAGIC POTION TO KNOCK GERIATRIX OUT!

WHAT'S THAT?

ALL THE SAME, A ROMAN WOULD HAVE TO BE PRETTY SURE OF HIMSELF TO ATTACK EVEN THIS OLD RELIC!

LOOK HERE...

AND LOOK AT THAT TINY LITTLE HELMET! THE LEGIONARY WHO WORE IT MUST HAVE BEEN A PROPER TITCH! WE ALWAYS KNEW GERIATRIX HAD SMALL LATIN...

...BUT SURELY EVEN GERIATRIX COULD HAVE MASTERED ANY LATIN THAT SMALL!

AND YOU KNOW WHAT GERIATRIX SAYS TO YOU?!?

WE MUST FIND OUT FOR SURE WHETHER THE ROMANS HAVE THE MAGIC POTION.

I'LL GO AND ASK THEM IF YOU LIKE.

NO, NOT YOU. UNHYGIENIX AND FULLIAUTOMATIX, YOU GO!

THEY'VE GOT IT!

THE ROMANS HAVE GOT THE MAGIC POTION! WE SAW THEM!

THAT'S RIDICULOUS! HOW COULD THEY HAVE MANAGED TO FIND OUT THE SECRET?

PUFF! PUFF!

WE'VE BEEN SEEING A LOT OF ROMANS AROUND THE VILLAGE LATELY.

ARE YOU ACCUSING ME OF GIVING THE ROMANS THE SECRET OF THE MAGIC POTION?

AND HOW ABOUT YOU, VITALSTATISTIX? ARE YOU ACCUSING ME OF TELLING ASTERIX THE SECRET – THE SECRET THAT MAY ONLY BE HANDED DOWN FROM DRUID TO DRUID, BY WORD OF MOUTH?

ER... WELL...

ALL RIGHT. I GET THE MESSAGE. I'M LEAVING THE VILLAGE.

ME TOO.

WELL, THEN, ME TOO.

WOOF!

BUT DRUID... IF YOU WALK OUT ON US WE WON'T HAVE ANY MAGIC POTION!

ALL YOU HAD TO DO WAS FALL IN IT WHEN YOU WERE BABIES!

SO THERE!

I WONDER IF WE MAY JUST POSSIBLY HAVE DONE A SILLY THING, BOYS...

YOU SHOULD HAVE STOPPED THEM, SENATOR.

STOP CALLING ME SENATOR, IDIOT! GET OUT OF MY SIGHT!

I FEEL VERY LOW...

ALL THE SAME, IT'S A PITY WE'RE LEAVING. NOW THE ROMANS HAVE GOT THE MAGIC POTION IT'LL BE MORE FUN.

THEY HAVEN'T GOT THE MAGIC POTION!

WHO HAS GOT THE MAGIC POTION, THEN?

DON'T LET IT BOTHER YOU, OBELIX.

NO ONE EVER EXPLAINS ANYTHING TO ME! THEY JUST KEEP ME AROUND BECAUSE I'M ORNAMENTAL!

GOOD MORNING, LEGIONARY. WE COME IN PEACE. WE WANT TO SEE THAT NEW ROMAN...

CONVOLVULUS, THE CIVIL SERVANT? THIRD TENT ON THE LEFT.

WHAT HAVE YOU GOT ON YOUR HEAD?

THEY'VE BEEN PRACTISING PSYCHOLOGY ON ME.

YOU AND DOGMATIX WAIT FOR US HERE, OBELIX.

RIGHT.

HEY!

QUID?

SNAP!

THERE'S SOMETHING I'D LIKE TO CHECK UP ON, IF YOU DON'T MIND...

CARRY ON.

PLAFF!

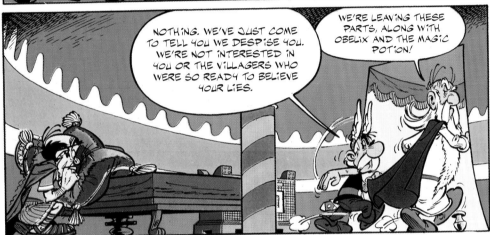

THEY HAVEN'T EVEN LEFT A SENTRY!

WHAT ARE WE GOING TO DO IN THIS CAMP IF THERE AREN'T ANY ROMANS LEFT?

AHA! THERE'S THEIR CAULDRON OF SO-CALLED MAGIC POTION!

YOU'RE GOING TO CARRY IT, OBELIX, WITHOUT SPILLING A DROP.

IS THIS MAGIC POTION?

MY DEAR OBELIX, IF YOU DRANK IT IT WOULDN'T HAVE ANY EFFECT ON YOU AT ALL.

OH, THEN IT IS MAGIC POTION. MAGIC POTION NEVER DOES HAVE ANY EFFECT ON ME AT ALL.

?

SOMETIMES HE MAKES ME WONDER IF I KNOW WHAT I MEAN MYSELF!

LET'S NOT WASTE TIME. WE HAVE TO REACH THE VILLAGE BEFORE THE ROMANS.

30

SURE ENOUGH, THE LEGIONARIES ARE PASSING THROUGH THE FOREST IN THE DIRECTION OF THE VILLAGE...

I SAY, THE LADS WANT TO KNOW HOW THE LOOT IS GOING TO BE SHARED OUT THIS TIME, BECAUSE AT MUNDA...

WELL, WHAT ABOUT MUNDA? WHAT HAPPENED AT MUNDA?

THE LOOT WAS PERFECTLY FAIRLY DISTRIBUTED... LET'S SEE, THERE WERE THOSE TWELVE VALUABLE VASES...

LET'S NOT COUNT ON VALUABLE VASES... YOU MIGHT GET A NASTY JAR!

SURE ENOUGH, IN THE VILLAGE, THE GAULS ARE GETTING READY TO PROVE THAT THEY ARE NOT BY ANY MEANS OLD CROCKS...

WITH OR WITHOUT POTION, **WE'LL SHOW THEM WHO WE ARE!**

WE'D BETTER NOT SHOW THEM HOW MANY WE ARE, THAT'S ALL!

38

THERE'S NOT A MOMENT TO BE LOST! THE GAULS KNOW THAT OUR POTION IS NO GOOD. THEIR DRUID IS GOING TO MAKE THEM SOME OF THE REAL STUFF! WE MUST ATTACK AT ONCE. IT'S OUR ONLY CHANCE!

ATTA...!?

WHERE'S THAT LOT GONE?

THE VANGUARD WENT TO HELP THE REAR, AND I STAYED AT THE FRONT BACK HERE, BECAUSE AFTER ALL PSYCHOLOGICAL WARFARE...

GO AND FIND ME ALL THOSE IDIOTS, IDIOT!

34A

MEANWHILE...

ALL RIGHT, SO WE BEHAVED BADLY. WE BELIEVED THE SLANDERS THAT ROMAN SPREAD, AND WE WERE WRONG... YOU WOULDN'T LET US DOWN NOW, WOULD YOU?

NEVER MIND! IT'LL BE LIKE GERGOVIA! WE DON'T NEED ANY POTION! LET'S GO!

HE'S RIGHT! LET'S GO!

I'M COMING TOO!

I DON'T KNOW WHERE YOU'RE GOING, BUT I'M GOING WITH YOU!

WE'LL ALL GO!

BIFF!

THIS IS MORE LIKE YOU! ABSOLUTELY CRAZY, BUT UNITED ONCE AGAIN. NOW I'LL MAKE YOU SOME MAGIC POTION! REAL MAGIC POTION!

34B

BUT THAT WILL TAKE TIME, AND THE ROMANS...

WELL, YOU AND OBELIX HOLD THE ROMANS OFF!

DO YOU GET IT, OBELIX? WE MUST HOLD THEM OFF UNTIL OUR DRUID HAS FINISHED MAKING THE MAGIC POTION.

I DON'T REALLY GET ANYTHING, BUT I'M WITH YOU ALL THE WAY!

SURRENDER, GAULS!

MAY I?

BY ALL MEANS.

BIFF!

CRASH!

PLONK!

KERPLONK!

BIFF!

BIFF!

RETIRE!

ASTERIX, WE MUST PRESS THEM TO STAY! IF THEY GO AWAY WE CAN'T HOLD THEM OFF!

NO, IT'S A PITY THE ROMAN TROOPS HAVE SUCH RETIRING DISPOSITIONS.

A WHOLE ARMY PUT TO FLIGHT BY TWO BARBARIANS. OH, WON'T CAESAR BE PLEASED WHEN I TELL HIM ABOUT THIS!

THERE ISN'T ANYTHING TO TELL. THIS IS A STRATEGIC WITHDRAWAL. I'M GOING TO ASK THE OTHER GARRISONS TO BRING UP REINFORCEMENTS AND TAKE THEM IN THE REAR. WE SHALL CRUSH THEM BY SHEER WEIGHT OF NUMBERS!

OF COURSE, THERE ARE TWO OF THEM, AND WE'RE ONLY ONE GARRISON.

TAKE THESE MESSAGES TO LAUDANUM, TOTORUM AND COMPENDIUM. HURRY!

SURE ENOUGH, TIME IS RUNNING OUT FOR THE ROMANS...

JUST LET IT SIMMER FOR A FEW MORE MINUTES...

THE BATTLE OF THE VILLAGE

Only a panoramic view can do justice to the complex nature of this terrible battle, in which a small village of indomitable Gauls comes to grips with the garrisons of the fortified Roman camps of Aquarium, Totorum, Laudanum and Compendium.

1 Indomitable little Gaulish village.
2 Garrison of Aquarium (Roman camp).
3 Garrison of Roman camp of Totorum.
4 Garrison of Roman camp of Laudanum.
5 Garrison of Roman camp of Compendium.
6, 7, 8, 9 Gauls pouring out of the village any old how, without any plan of battle.
10 Druid Getafix awaiting the outcome of the battle beside his cauldron, now empty.
11 Bard Cacofonix asking the druid what it's all about, and what, might he ask, is going on?
12 Pirate ship sunk by Gauls pouring out at (8) full of enthusiasm, discovering on arrival at the beach that there are no Romans available, and deciding not to waste their time anyway, by Toutatis.
13 Obelix, menhir delivery man, trying to keep back the Gauls while explaining to them that he got there first, he didn't ring for anyone, he would like to be left alone with his own Romans and they don't want to be disturbed.
14 Fulliautomatix, village blacksmith.
15 Unhygienix, village fishmonger, friend of the afore-mentioned.
16 Point of intersection of the two friends.
17 Geriatrix, village elder, engaged in single combat with Magnumopus, Roman legionary.
18 Vitalstatistix, chief of the Gaulish village, badly let down by his shield-bearers, who have jumped the fence without bothering to see that he kept his balance. He feels understandably downcast for a few moments.

GAULISH VILLAGE
COMPENDIUM
LAUDANUM
TOTORUM
AQUARIUM

MAGNUMOPUS Roman legionary

CONVOLVULUS Roman strategist

PLATYPUS Roman centurion

OBELIX menhir delivery man

ASTERIX Gaulish warrior

VITALSTATISTIX Gaulish chief

SPQR

THE BATTLE, ALTHOUGH VIOLENT, IS OF SHORT DURATION, AND THE VICTORS ARE LEFT IN POSSESSION OF THE BATTLEFIELD, THEIR ARMS FULL OF TROPHIES...

TEEHEEHEE!

SLAP! SLAP!

I CALL THAT BATTLE A REAL SUCCESS; IT WAS A GREAT CRUSH!

YES, BUT THERE'S STILL SOMETHING WE HAVE TO DO. CALL THE OTHERS!

A LITTLE FARTHER AWAY...

OH, SO THERE YOU ARE. YOU AND YOUR TROUBLEMAKING! BRAVO! OH, VERY WELL DONE! WE WERE GOING ALONG QUIETLY AS USUAL, THE GAULS WERE MINDING THEIR OWN BUSINESS, AND NOW WE'VE SUFFERED A DEFEAT, THANKS TO YOU!

AS FOR ME, I DID WHAT I HAD TO DO... IT WAS YOU OTHERS WHO...

HEY!

!!!

ALL RIGHT, I'M GOING... I'M NOT NEEDED HERE ANY MORE...

LEGIONARIES! ARREST THAT PERSON!

43

THANKS VERY MUCH, CONVOLVULUS!

?

I BEG YOUR PARDON?

YOU DID WELL! WE'RE PLEASED WITH YOU. YOU KEPT YOUR WORD!

YOU'LL ALWAYS FIND A WELCOME IN OUR VILLAGE, CONVOLVULUS!

AND HERE'S A LITTLE SOUVENIR OVER AND ABOVE THE PRICE WE SETTLED...

LONG LIVE CONVOLVULUS!

UP WITH CONVOLVULUS!

UP WITH OUR OLD PAL!

BUT... BUT...

HA! NOW I SEE IT ALL! YOU WERE ON THEIR SIDE ALL THE TIME! THAT EXPLAINS OUR DEFEAT!

I NEVER! IT'S A SLANDER! YOU CAN'T BELIEVE SUCH WICKED LIES!

OH, CAN'T WE JUST!!!

CRASH!

PUT HIM IN CHAINS! WE'LL BE SENDING HIM BACK TO ROME TO CAESAR, CHARGED WITH HIGH TREASON!

BUT WE NEED NOT BE UNDULY WORRIED ABOUT THE TROUBLEMAKER; CONVOLVULUS WILL WRIGGLE HIS WAY OUT OF ANYTHING AND EVEN ON BOARD THE GALLEY WHICH IS TAKING HIM BACK TO ROME, HE DOES NOT FEEL ALONE... SLANDER, JEALOUSY AND CALUMNY HAVE EMBARKED WITH HIM!

I SAID TO PORT!

STOP SHOVING YOUR OAR IN, CAPTAIN – WE ALL KNOW THE SORT OF PULL YOU USED TO GET YOUR JOB!

WE'VE BEHAVED BADLY TOWARDS YOU, ASTERIX; OUR FRIENDSHIP SHOULD HAVE BEEN PROOF AGAINST ANY SLANDERS. YOU AND GETAFIX AND OBELIX HAVE TAUGHT US A LESSON, AND YOU HAVE SAVED OUR VILLAGE BY BANISHING DISCORD FROM IT...

ASTERIX, WE BOW TO YOU!

NO, I DO THE BOWING, **NOT YOU!!!!**

SOMETIMES HE ACTS IN THE MOST UNBALANCED WAY!

IF HE CARRIES ON LIKE THIS WE'LL LET HIM DOWN ONE OF THESE DAYS!

FORGIVE US, ASTERIX!

LET BYGONES BE BYGONES! WE'LL ORGANIZE A BIRTHDAY FEAST FOR OUR CHIEF! A REAL ONE, NOT A FLOP LIKE LAST TIME!

BRAVO, BY TOUTATIS!

I'M GOING TO GIVE HIM ANOTHER MENHIR!

I'M GOING TO GIVE HIM A SWORD!

I CAUGHT A GOOD FISH LAST WEEK. IT'LL BE JUST WHAT HE WANTED!

IT WILL BE A LOVELY SURPRISE FOR THE CHIEF!

MEANWHILE...

WHAT A WONDERFUL SURPRISE! MY DEAR FRIENDS, I AM AT A LOSS FOR WORDS...

I'M GLAD WE'RE ALL FRIENDS AGAIN!

ALL THE SAME, I'D LIKE TO KNOW IF THEY REALLY ARE CURED.

I MUST SAY, IT WOULD BE INTERESTING TO FIND OUT... AND IT'S ABOUT TIME YOU GOT A BIT OF YOUR OWN BACK.

45

NEXT MORNING...

UNHYGIENIX FISHMO

OH, LOOK AT THAT!

WHAT ARE THEY UP TO?

ONLY THE CHIEF IS ALLOWED TO TRAVEL ABOUT THAT WAY.

PERHAPS HE'S GOING TO REPLACE THE CHIEF?

I EXPECT VITALSTATISTIX APPOINTED HIM HIS SUCCESSOR AFTER THE BATTLE.

IF THERE'S GOING TO BE A SUCCESSOR IT OUGHT TO BE MY HUSBAND, GERIATRIX. AFTER ALL, HE'S GOT MORE EXPERIENCE THAN ANYONE ELSE!

GERIATRIX? THAT'S NOT EXPERIENCE, THAT'S SENILITY! NOW LOOK AT FULLIAUTOMATIX – YOUNG, STRONG AND...

BACTERIA! PUT AWAY THE FISH – QUICK!

FULLIAUTOMATIX? THAT GREAT OAF? NOW MY HUSBAND HAS A GOOD HEAD FOR BUSINESS, A...

GOOD MORNING!

UNHY

HERE! YOU STAND IN THE QUEUE LIKE EVERYONE ELSE!

BUT I'M THE CHIEF'S WIFE!

NO, I'M THE CHIEF'S WIFE! SERVE ME, BACTERIA!

?!

SPLATCH!

46

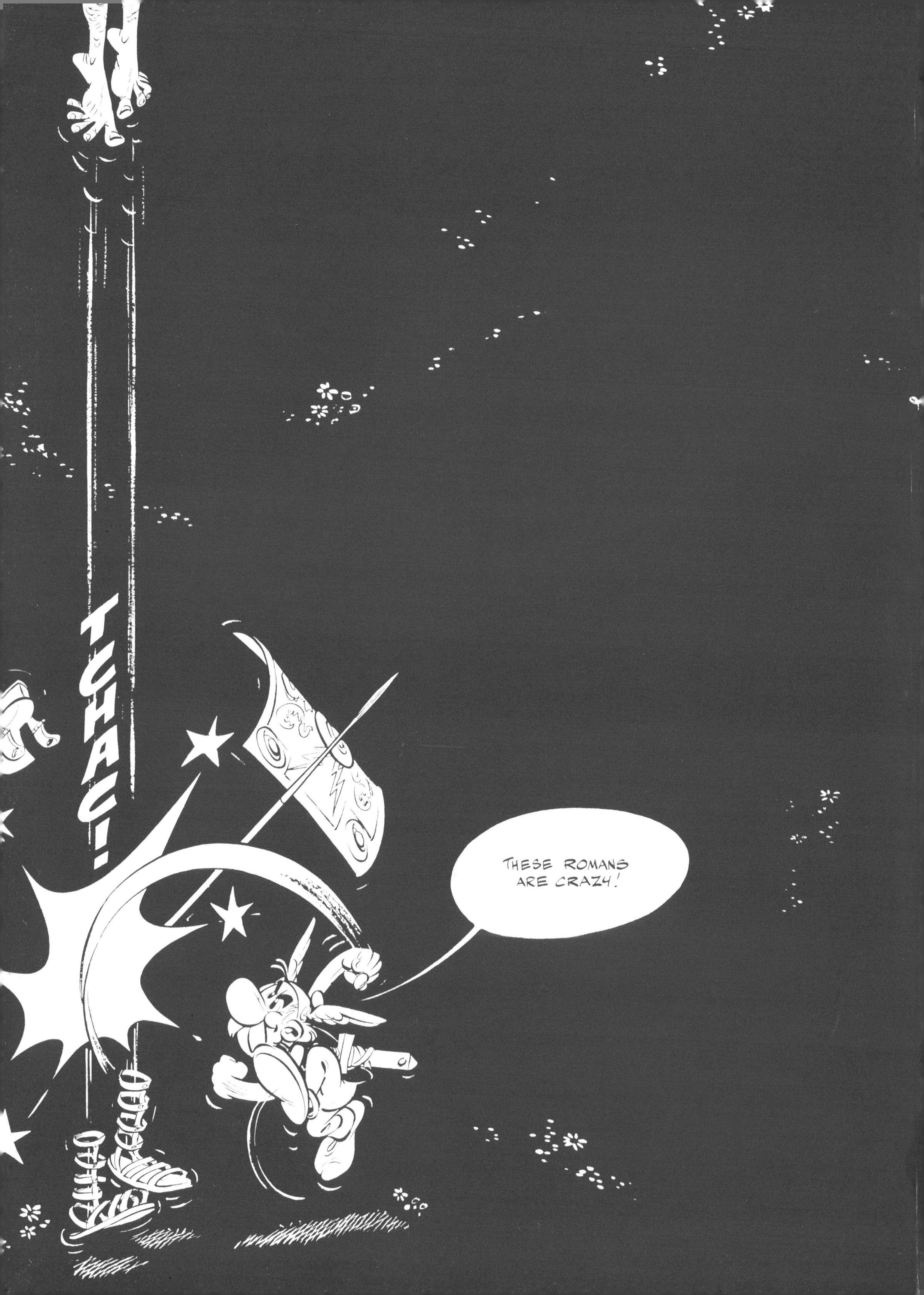
TCHAC!
THESE ROMANS ARE CRAZY!